KU-598-425

Aphrodisiacs

Aphrodisiacs
From A to Z

BY

Peter and Mary Harrison

Jupiter Books : London

First published in 1979 by
JUPITER BOOKS (LONDON) LIMITED
167 Hermitage Road, London N4 1LZ

Copyright © Peter and Mary Harrison 1979.

ISBN 0 906379 06 7

Composed on the Linotype-Paul VIP in 12-point
Garamond and printed and bound in Great Britain
by Tonbridge Printers Limited at their
Peach Hall Works, Tonbridge, Kent.

Introduction

THE GODDESS OF LOVE – Aphrodite – started it all. The word 'aphrodisiac', meaning 'any form of sexual stimulation' was derived from her name.

Aphrodite was the Greek goddess of beauty and fruitfulness, as well as love. She was identified by the Romans as Venus, and had a frothy and fruity birth, as 'she rose from the sea where Uranus' sex organ had fallen, after he had been mutilated by crows.'

Our heroine had one husband and five lovers, including the handsome Adonis, making for a very active love life. Whether or not she had any favourite aphrodisiac is not recorded, but it can be assumed that because of her phallic start in life, she was a gonner for the penis – and probably the larger variety! On the whole, a very accommodating lady.

Aphrodisiacs come in two main groups:—

    1)   External – i.e. visual and aural aphrodisiacs and those
includes pornography – books, films, etc.

    2)   Internal – i.e. alcohol, food, love potions and medical preparations.

Although under separate groupings, most aphrodisiacs work together, which means that although it might come into the second category, any particular item would also have influences stemming from the first category, intermingling with the senses and creating a heightened sexual experience. Think of a really appetising meal. You get the visual satisfaction and stimulation, interest arising from the aroma, and the gratifying taste, which together bring on a general feeling of well-being which is conducive to sensual feelings. Eating a rich, savory meal is one of the more subtle ways of taking an aphrodisiac. The other extreme is Spanish Fly, which has been known to prove fatal. In the sixteenth century, a chap drunk two drams of Spanish Fly and it made his so rampant that he was on top of his wife no less than eighty-seven times over two nights, and even when his doctor was examining him, he ejaculated three times. Before any wife starts looking up the Spanish Fly ingredients so that she can give it to her old man, be warned — as little as 1.5 grammes can kill him. On the other hand — what a way to go!

This is a fun book written so that you and your partner(s) can have lots of tittilating fun and games. Have a good time, time and time again.

PETER & MARY HARRISON

Kensington, 1979

Aphrodisiacs

A

ABRICOTINE A type of apricot brandy which is distilled in France, the country famous for lovers.

ABSINTHE This is a green liqueur also known as 'wormwood juice', **WORMWOOD** being a nickname for *Artemisia Absinthium* the plant from which absinthe is obtained. This is a bush with silky stems and small yellow flowers, found in waste areas such as hedges and ditches. Common all over Europe and in particular, France. The extract from the plant is mixed with anise, the former giving a bitter-sweet quality to the liqueur. Remember the old saying . . . 'Absence makes the heart grow fonder' . . . In this case absinthe definitely makes not only the heart grow fonder, but every other part of the anatomy as well.

ACORUS CALAMUS An aromatic herb known as 'Venus's plant' used to promote erotic practices.

ADRENOCHROME A highly dangerous drug which can produce erotic hallucinations. This should not be used without medical advice.

ADVOCAAT This drink is especially potent in its effects on the emotions and sexual drive, because of the combination of alcohol and eggs which are in themselves aphrodisiacs. Advocaat is also considered a good health drink and a tonic which helps to create a feeling of general well-being.

ALCHONE This is a herb, also known as 'polignonia', from which a highly potent juice is extracted, taken in some countries for its ability to stir up sexual tendencies.

ALCOHOL Because of the intoxicating properties of alcohol and its ability to break down inhibitions it is one of the most common aphrodisiacs. Some alcoholic drinks are more effective than others, such as BRANDY and VODKA. All liqueurs have strong aphrodisiac qualities especially when they are taken after a nutritious and satisfying meal, creating a warm glow and loving atmosphere.

ALLSPICE A PIMENTO or Jamaican pepper which sets the flesh tingling and raises the spirits – among other things.

ALMONDS Aphrodisiacs both when taken by themselves – as is the case with most nuts – and also when mixed into love foods and philtres. A favourite combination is almonds and honey. An old love-provoking potion consists of grated almonds and honey in hot water with a few grains of pine cone added. This is widely believed to create a wild sexual urge.

ALOES A bitter drug which is obtained from aloes-wood, and used for medicinal purposes. A famous mediaeval love potion.

ALPINE A plant found on mountain tops and renowned for bringing heightened pleasure to affairs of the flesh.

AMARANTH A yellow or purple flower which was exchanged by mediaeval lovers as a token of never-ending affection, nicknamed 'Love-lies-bleeding'.

AMBERGRIS A wax-like substance found in the tropical seas. Widely used in the Orient as an aphrodisiac, mainly in the preparation of love sweets and erotic confectionery. It is sometimes used as a perfume and at one time was very popular in France.

ANCHOVY Latin lovers thrive on anchovies which are noted for the strong effect they have upon the emotions.

ANEMONE A love herb believed to bring excitement to all amatory indulgences.

ANGEL WATER Popular as a love potion in the eighteenth century. A mixture of rose water, myrtle water and orange blossom water, some distilled musk spirit and a dash of AMBERGRIS were the ingredients of the love philtre known as 'Angel Water'. This drink was often served at peasant weddings and was believed to set the happy couple off on a flying start to their honeymoon.

ANISEED The seed of the 'anise' which is an aromatic plant with a peculiarly delicate perfume. Aniseed is used for flavouring in cooking and also for preparing a liqueur called 'anisette', a strong love potion which stirs up bodily lust.

ANJANIKA A Hindu plant which is used in the making of a powerful love potion which has a reputation for awakening desire for sexual activity.

ANT In Central Europe, the winged ant was sometimes used in place of the black beetle in the making of CANTHARIDES – better known as SPANISH FLY. It was also used extensively for medicinal purposes.

APHRODISIAC SOUP Powder some almonds, and mix with two egg yolks. Add half a pint of chicken stock. Bring to the boil, then simmer gently for ten minutes. Just before serving, pour on fresh cream.

APHRODISIAC WINE Any good wine can be used as the base, then add a few drops of vanilla essence, a pinch of ginger, a pinch of cinnamon, and some strained rhubarb juice.

APPLE Probably the oldest known aphrodisiac in the world because of the associations with Adam and Eve.

ARABIC A gum resin which is reputed to have aphrodisiac properties especially in Eastern countries.

ARECA PALM A type of palm tree from which the BETEL NUT is obtained. This was a popular ingredient in ancient Greek love philtres.

ARRACK A spirit which is made from the heavily sugared flowers of the MOH tree found in Oriental countries, and when flavoured with fruits and herbs, causes the passions to be aroused.

ARROWROOT A plant found in the West Indies from which is obtained a highly nutritious starchy substance, believed to be a love stimulant. Used extensively in cookery.

ARTEMISIA A plant that grows in several different forms and has a flowering head. An ingredient can be extracted from the plant called 'Santonin'. This is highly active when mixed with food or drinks and can have the effect of arousing sexual desire.

ARTICHOKE These have always been considered high on the list of strong aphrodisiacs. Part of the reason for their popularity is probably attributed to the fact that the artichoke possesses a strange heating characteristic. In the past it was considered that any food which is hot must surely enflame the passions. This belief was particularly widespread in France where mediaeval Parisian street vendors used the aphrodisiac qualities of the artichoke to enhance their sales. It was quite common to hear the vendors' voices screeching out the merits of the plant, drawing special attention to the fact that . . . 'Artichokes! . . . Artichokes! . . . Heast the body and the spirit – heats the genitals!'.

ASPARAGUS Believed to be an aphrodisiac, especially in Arab countries where they boil it then fry it in egg yolks to produce a powerful feeling of lust.

AUBERGINE The fruit of the EGG-PLANT, purple in colour and believed to have aphrodisiac properties.

A – VITAMIN For a strong sex drive it is essential to feel in good physical condition. This vitamin is plentiful in green vegetables, milk, cream cheese, fish-liver oil, liver and kidney. It is essential for healthy growth and the structure and functioning of the skin and mucous membrane. The sex organs perform more efficiently when well nourished, thus giving heightened pleasure to the parties concerned.

AVOCADO PEAR Rich in health-giving minerals and vitamins, these fruits not only feed the body but also the imagination due to their shape and the thought-association with the female breast.

B

BAMBOO This large reed from India can be regarded as an aphrodisiac because of its shape. Huts and furniture can be made from this light strong substance.

BANANA As well as being a highly sustaining food, the banana is used as an aphrodisiac because of its phallic shape. In olden days, girls and women in Edinburgh used bananas and other fruit for sexual purposes to such an extent that chastity corsets were introduced. These consisted of a tight garment adorned with nets and padlocks in such a manner that access to the sexual organs became quite impossible.

BANISTERIA CAAPI A plant which is found in South America from which the drug HARMINE is obtained. This is a highly dangerous drug which is taken in the form of a tea made from the leaves of the plant. It produces hallucinations of an erotic nature.

BANYAN A type of fig tree found in India the branches of which tend to spread out and then take root. This sort of reproducing characteristic is responsible for the banyan being associated with the aphrodisiac theme.

BARBEL A fish often used for medicinal purposes, in particular for the case of waning virility.

BASIL The eighteenth-century method of using basil was to crush the seeds and then extract the juice. This was then put up the nostrils, and was believed to promote sexual urges in both the male and the female.

BEAN The seed of various types of leguminous plants, it is high in protein content, and associated with life and vitality, hence the saying 'full of beans'. Also there is the mental connection with the bean and the female sex organ. It is believed that St. Jerome forbade nuns to eat beans because they were thought to excite the genitals.

BEEF It is accepted all over the world that red meat plays an important part in maintaining a healthy and active sex life. The high protein content acts as a strength-giver which encourages extra performance and virility.

BEER One of the oldest sexual stimulants known to arouse the carnal desires. It is believed by some, that excessive beer drinking is a sign of excessive masculinity.

BEETROOT A plant with a ball-shaped root from which sugar is extracted. Commonly served in salads because of its attractive deep red colour. It is looked upon as an aphrodisiac because of its shape and the association with the sexual organs.

BELLADONNA This is prepared from the poisonous plant called 'Deadly Nightshade'. It is a strong drug used for medicinal purposes and it contains properties which excite and arouse the emotions.

BENEDICTINE The tonic liqueur which fires the imagination and causes the sexual system to adopt an aroused state which is conducive to passionate love-making. As the name suggests, it is a blessing to all who indulge in this drink. 'Benedict', the name for a newly-married man, stems from the same source.

BETEL NUT The nut of an ARECA PALM tree which was ground down and used in the making of love potions by the ancient Greeks and Romans.

BHANG The Sanskrit word for hemp. In India, it is believed that sexual capacity can be increased by chewing the leaves and seeds. Sometimes a potion is taken which is made by mixing the seeds with sugar and musk then adding a little ambergris.

BHUYA-KOKALI A Hindu plant which is reputed to possess aphrodisiac qualities. Sometimes the juice is mixed with honey, sugar and clarified butter, and eaten as a delicacy.

BIOSTRATH A great herbal tonic which can be added to drinks such as VODKA or BRANDY and thus increases the aphrodisiac properties of the drink.

BIRD'S NEST SOUP This dish is highly thought of by the Chinese as being an effective aphrodisiac, possibly because of the association between the bird's nest and eggs which are famous for their love-stirring qualities.

BIRTHWORT A shrub which was widely used as an aphrodisiac by the Romans. It was popular in this country in mediaeval times.

BRAIN The brains of certain animals including calves, pigs and sheep are said to have strong aphrodisiac properties, and are most popular in the southern European countries.

BRANDY The famous drink enjoyed by the masters of love-making, the French. Because brandy is distilled from wine, it takes on the romantic and passionate qualities of the wine and multiplies them to a high degree. A favourite love-evoking combination is brandy and egg yolks.

BRUSSICA ERUCA Otherwise known as ROCKET. A type of cabbage which is found in the Mediterranean regions and used extensively as a salad food. Very strong amatory powers are attributed to this food which was popular with the Romans.

BREWER'S YEAST Because this is rich in Vitamin B12, it is an established treatment for infertility. It is known that many couples who were unable to produce children were given the brewer's yeast treatment, and have since become happy parents. Not the least of this substance's attractions is it's incredible rising power.

BROCCOLI This vegetable contains the essential B2 vitamin and is part of the same family as cabbages and cauliflowers. Believed to have some powers as an aphrodisiac.

BULBOUS ROOTS All plants having bulb-shaped roots have a certain amount of aphrodisiac qualities because of the thought-suggestions that are conjured up in the mind, and their relation to the genitals.

BUNNY EARS A small rubber band with two little rubber ears which when worn on the head of the penis adds to the excitement of the sex act. The device can also be used as a clitoral or vaginal stimulator.

BURGUNDY The blood-red wine of passion. Throughout the ages men and women have 'come' together over the red wine which enflames the passions and leads to sexual encounters.

BUTTER In some countries butter was looked upon as a two-fold aphrodisiac. Firstly it could be consumed and this was thought to heighten desire, and secondly it could be massaged into the body to give a feeling of excitement which would lead to amatory practices.

BUTTERMILK The liquid that remains after the churning process has been completed in the making of butter. This can be consumed as a health drink and it can also be applied to the skin as a beautifier.

B-VITAMIN The B-vitamins, in particular Vitamin B2, are necessary for a good sex life because they are involved in the production of sperm and the mating urge. Thiamine and RIBOFLAVIN which are obtained from the B-vitamins help to maintain potency. Foods rich in the B-vitamins include: yeast, wheatgerm, eggs, milk, liver, meat, soya beans, green vegetables, peanuts, spinach, fish and fowl.

C

CABBAGE A leafy green vegetable which is commonly used for its high vitamin content. The juice of a cooked cabbage can be added to drinks and can produce a fun-loving frame of mind.

CACTUS The name given to a wide variety of prickly plants found mostly in Mexico and desert regions. One particular type of cactus is *peyote* from which is obtained the drug MESCALINE. This is highly dangerous and should not be used without medical supervision. It produces erotic sensations but can cause extensive emotional damage.

CALABASH A very large fruit encased in a hard shell, the produce of the calabash tree. The gourd can be used as a drinking vessel or cooking utensil and was used for serving the love potions made from the fibres of the fruit mixed with honey.

CALAMINT A herb in India which is believed to stir up the sexual desires. A paste can be made by mixing the shredded leaves with cream and this is reputed to have a double use – firstly it can be eaten, and secondly it can be smeared over the body.

CALCIUM This is a metallic element which is essential for general good health and an interest in sex.

CALISAIA The name given to the bark of a tree found in Peru which is pounded and served with the juice of bitter oranges. This drink is reputed to possess powers to coax the senses into a mood for sex.

CAMEL'S MILK Believed to be an aphrodisiac especially in Arab countries where it is taken to improve sexual performance and increase the animal urge.

CAMPHOR This oil has strong aromatic characteristics and is strangely alluring, although it can become overbearing. It is the ingredient used in the making of moth-balls. Very popular in Italy.

CANNABIS Short for *Cannabis Sativa*, a well-known drug which is made from the oil extracted from the flowers of Indian hemp, grown in Asia, Africa, North America and the Himalayas. The drug can be made up in varying strengths under many different names. For instance if it is smoked or eaten in pure form as it is extracted from the plant, it is called *charas*. If it is powdered down and sifted it becomes HASHISH, and if taken in a weaker liquid form it is known as BHANG. In Mexico the drug is called MARIJUANA. Cannabis is a strong narcotic.

CANNELLONI This dish from romantic Italy is reminiscent of long hot sultry Italian summers where passion is second nature.

CANTHARIDES Better known as SPANISH FLY, this is

probably the most notorious of all aphrodisiacs. It is a drink made from the *Cantharis Vesicatoria* beetle found in southern Europe which is dried and powdered. It was introduced to Europe from the Orient at the time of the Crusades. It has the power to arouse the sexual urge by acute irritation of the gastro-intestinal system and by dilation of the blood vessels, all of which stimulate the genitals. It has strong lust-inducing qualities, but there is an element of danger as it can cause difficulty in urinating, blood-stained urine, and excruciating pain. It is believed that Spanish Fly is a poison and in fact it has been known that as little as 1·5 grammes can prove fatal — what a way to go! This is one of the limited number of aphrodisiacs that are recognised by modern science. It can be bought in sex-aid shops in tablet form.

CARAWAY Very popular in the Orient as an aphrodisiac. It can be used in many different ways but perhaps it is most widely used in cake-making, where the caraway seeds give a distinctive flavour.

CARDAMOM This is a hot seed in a kind of shell. The seeds can be used in dishes such as biriani and curried foods. It gives a warm feeling of anticipation.

CARDOON A plant resembling the artichoke in appearance. The leaves are believed to be an aphrodisiac and are very popular in France.

CARROT This phallus-shaped vegetable has been looked upon for centuries as being a stimulant and is used not only internally but also externally by frustrated females because of its resemblance to the shape of the penis.

CASTOR OIL A lubricant which is believed to arouse hidden urges when massaged onto the skin. The American Indians used this extensively for amatory purposes.

CAVIARE The name given to the roe of the STURGEON fish which has been salted. This is looked upon as an exclusive delicacy. The sea-connections and the suggestion that this food is indeed something special promotes a sensation of grandeur leading to powerful love-making.

CELATION Ch3 Plus. This is a great help to people who are emotionally cold and who find difficulty in making love. It has the power to melt down inhibitions, relax the nerves, and warm the cockles of the heart. It can be found in health food shops.

CELERY This vegetable with the long juicy stalk is thought of as resembling the penis and has the power to evoke deep sexual feelings. It is one of the favourite foods of the rabbit, and everyone knows about the mating habits of rabbits.

CHAMPAGNE The fun drink of all time. Forever associated with life, laughter and love. This delightful drink stimulates the senses into a bubble of lust.

CHARTREUSE This is a very strong liqueur which comes in two forms, green and yellow. It is the latter, the yellow chartreuse which has the reputation for being a hell-raiser. Just one sip can blow the mind.

CHEESE An old favourite for supplying the necessary protein and stamina and thus encouraging love play.

CHERRY The small red fleshy fruit full of titillation and resembling the female nipple.

CHERVIL A herb which contains an aromatic property which when taken in food results in heightened sensations and sensuality.

CHESTNUT The Elizabethans believed that chestnuts had aphrodisiac properties because they looked like testicles. They became common playthings amongst courtesans who used to tie them to the end of a piece of string and play a game similar to that of the yoyo.

CHICKEN The association between the chicken and the egg and the reproductive organs gives the chicken its aphrodisiac characteristics. Added to this, the chicken contains Vitamin E which is regarded as the love and sex vitamin.

CHILLI PEPPER Known for its extra hot taste the chilli pepper is the main ingredient of the romantic dish *chilli con carne* which sets the soul ablaze with lust.

CHIVE A herb of the onion family believed to increase sexual desire.

CHUTNEY A mixture of various fruits, spices, vegetables and herbs which can enflame the mind with uncontrollable desire for love-making.

CIDER The golden drink, made from apples. A great favourite in the south-west of England. It is plentiful, cheap and highly potent. It stirs the inner senses to a point of no return.

CINCHONA The bark of a tree which is found in Peru and mashed down to a pulp to make a health drink. It is said to encourage the flow of love juice and make the participants swim in a sea of ecstasy.

CINNAMON This can be obtained either in stick form or powdered. It comes from Ceylon trees and is in fact the bark of the tree. It is light brown in colour and fairly hot. It is often chewed or smoked, producing sensual excitement.

CIVET This is the perfume made from the secretions of the civet-cat. As well as being worn externally, civet was used in France in the eighteenth century to flavour confectionery. If a gentleman offered a lady a civet-drop he could be assured of many sweet nights of love.

CLOVE The dried flower bud of a tropical tree which is used as a spice and will add spice to love-life. It is extensively used in cooking because of its delicate flavour, especially in apple tarts. A couple of cloves in hot whisky leaves a warming love glow.

COCAINE A highly charged dangerous drug which should never be used without medical supervision. It has been known to excite women into sexual fits and uncontrollable lust. It has an aphrodisiac effect on men but to a lesser degree.

COCKLE BREAD This is a concoction which no longer is in

common use but was very popular in mediaeval England. It took the form of a cake, the main ingredient of which was menstrual blood.

COD LIVER OIL A very versatile substance which can be used in many ways both for medicinal and culinary purposes, not to mention the frolics of the bedroom.

COINTREAU An orange-flavoured liqueur which leaves a hot delicious tingling sensation in the mouth.

COLEWORT A herb which is believed to induce a love trance. It was enjoyed to a great extent by the Romans in their celebrated orgies.

CORRIANDER This is a delicately perfumed aromatic seed which is used a lot in eastern countries. When added to food such as curry, it gives a zest to the meal which leaves a warm, pleasant feeling, ripe for sexual pleasure. Arabian knights looked upon this as a love potion, when brewed with honey and water.

COW WHEAT Properly known as *Melampryum Pratense,* this is a tall flowering plant which is used to feed cows, hence the name 'cow wheat'. It is said to promote amatory excitement.

CRAB Together with cod, crayfish, cockles and clams, crabs are highly reputed for their stimulant qualities because of their connection with the sea, the birthplace of Aphrodite the goddess of love.

CRAB APPLE Said to make the sex glands work overtime. These small apples can be made into a jelly and used in many love-provoking ways.

CREAM Besides the fact that fresh cream is a delicious food, it acts as an aphrodisiac due to its appearance. Being thick, white and creamy, its resemblance to sperm works many women into a highly aroused state.

CRÈME DE MENTHE The famous green liqueur which as its name suggests, is 'cream of mint'. Here we have a combination of the cream suggestion and the aromatic plant MINT, which together make a giddy sexual pair.

CRESS A garnishing plant found in old ruins and guaranteed to put new life into a sagging love affair. Cress juice is an excellent health drink and when mixed with honey and ginger can have an extreme effect on the emotions.

CROWN A gadget which is worn on the head of the penis during love-making, and adds extra ecstasy to the act. It is a round rubber bubble which has a rubber frill at the base, designed to tickle the fancy.

CUBEB A pepper berry from which a highly exciting drink can be made. Hailed by the Arabs as a sure-fire love potion. Used in medicine and cookery.

CUCUMBER Due to its phallic shape, this vegetable awakes deep carnal desires. Its long fleshy appearance sets the imagination on fire.

CUMIN A plant used extensively in Indian cookery and believed to bring on waves of ecstasy when used in food served with an aphrodisiac wine.

CURRY Hot Indian dish consisting mainly of meat cooked with a variety of spices. Well known to spice up an affair.

CYCLAMEN A root which was powdered down and mixed with wine and honey to produce a powerful love potion.

D

DAMIANA This is obtained from the plant known as *Turnera Diffusia* which is mostly found in Brazil. Guaranteed to fire the blood with an unquenchable thirst for sex.

DANDELION WINE A wine which conjures up the wild open spaces and leads the imagination on a trip through fantasies of the flesh.

DARNEL A grass which was used in a porridge-like meal together with barley and certain aromatic gums such as frankincense and MYRRH. This concoction was taken as a sexual stimulant particularly by women in the Orient.

DATE The sweet fruit of the palm tree. It has a large single stone inside the fleshy sphere, and bears a resemblance to the testicles thus giving it its name as an aphrodisiac.

DEVIL FLESH The name given by the Spaniards who invaded Mexico to the plant *peyote* of the cactus family from which is obtained the dangerous drug MESCALINE. This causes hallucinations of a horrific nature, also erotic sensations.

DIASATYRION This is a root which can be mashed down and mixed with wine. If the drink is taken each morning and night for a week the effect on the sexual inclinations is said to be quite striking.

DILDO An imitation penis which can be strapped to the waist. This is not used by lesbians to take the place of the man's role in the sex act. But greatly favoured by suburban swingers.

DILL This is a herb which can be broken up and mixed with its own seed to form a most potent drink. When taken, it promotes a healthy appetite for lusty love-making.

DOG STONES An aphrodisiac plant of the SATYRION family that is believed to be highly effective when taken regularly in food or drinks.

DOVE The age-old symbol of love. In many countries the brains of the dove are specially prepared for wedding breakfasts. It is believed that if this dish is eaten by the bride and groom they can look forward to many happy years of love together.

DRAGON'S BLOOD The name given to a plant which used to be wrapped in paper and exchanged by lovers as a love charm. It was believed that if the charm was kept, the heart would remain true.

DRAMBUIE The thick sweet Scottish liqueur supposed to have been handed down from the days of Bonnie Prince Charlie who got himself quite a reputation with the ladies. The drink is whisky-based and is warm and intoxicating, causing a right royal come-on.

DREPANG A type of sea-slug found in the Red Sea. It has a peculiar resemblance to the penis even to the extent of becoming enlarged when touched by human hand. The Arabs look upon it as a powerful aphrodisiac.

DUCK A dish highly regarded by the Chinese who have always believed that the duck held a special magical property in connection with sexual stimulation.

DUFZ A perfume worn by Arabs and believed to excite the senses into a mood ripe for love-making.

DUMPLING These were very popular in the north of England and because of their shape and weight the similarity arose between dumplings and testicles.

E

EEL In the eighteenth century, French eels were considered to be such a strong sex food that they were ultimately banned as being too dangerous for the unsuspecting diner to eat. It was believed that they led the way to a life of sin and debauchery.

EGG Eggs have always been considered one of the main aphrodisiacs because of their association with reproduction. Also there is the similarity between the egg white and the male semen, and the egg yolk and the female eggs. Innumerable dishes can be made from eggs, also drinks such as ADVOCAAT and egg flips. In France, the yolk of an egg taken in cognac is supposed to work wonders for the sex life.

EGG-PLANT The plant which bears the purple AUBERGINE fruit believed to possess powers to produce excitement of a sexual nature.

ELDERBERRY WINE A delightful drink made from the berries of the white-flowered elder tree which is especially rich in pith, thus giving an increased sex appetite when fermented.

ENDIVE A curly-leaved edible plant highly favoured by the German *Fräuleins* who used to wear a spray of the leaves on their bosoms to encourage indifferent lovers to melt.

ERITHRAICON A member of the SATYRION family, this plant is attributed with great powers of stimulation which bring on unbridled lust.

ERYNGO *Eryngium Martimum,* a herb which resembles a thistle with blue flowers and a fleshy root, also known as 'sea holly'. The root is powdered down and used for flavouring food. The aphrodisiac association goes back to the days of Shakespeare.

EUPHORBIUM The gum which is extracted from a South American plant and believed to create a forceful feeling for sex.

EUPHORIA A state of sensuous reaction conclusive to sexual expression which is brought on by various aphrodisiacs.

E-VITAMIN This is popularly known as the 'vitality vitamin' because it is essential for an active sex life. Its job is to reduce the fat content of the blood and oxygenate the tissues. Wheat-germ capsules can be taken to provide the daily requirements of Vitamin E. This vitamin is also available in seed-germ oils, egg yolks, green vegetables and milk.

F

FALERNIA A drink which is said to have extra-special powers to heighten the sexual urge. In the eighteenth century it was a widely-used aphrodisiac. It was also a favourite love potion of the Romans.

FENNEL A yellow-flowered fragrant herb which accentuates the positive sexual feelings. Used in soup-making or as a sauce and highly recommended as a health food.

FIG Soft fruit not unlike the shape of testicles and known to create a strange amorous sensation, especially when eaten with cream.

FISH Due to the association with the goddess of love Venus, or Aphrodite, as the Greeks named her, all fish have a certain aphrodisiac quality attributed to them. This is based on the belief that Aphrodite rose from the sea. The name is derived from the Greek term *aphro* which means 'foam'.

FLEA-WORT A plant from which was extracted a sap believed to promote conception. In Roman times it was a custom that if two people drank a potion made from the sap three times a day for a month, they could be assured of conceiving a male child.

FOLIATUM An erotic ointment used by the Romans which was prepared from a substance called SPIKENARD, obtained from a plant found in the East.

FRANGIPANE A sex stimulant popular in Italy where it is served in pastry form with almonds and spices.

FRENCH ONION SOUP This is a strong aphrodisiac due to the combination of onions and alcohol which the French believe can lead to long nights of love.

FROGS' LEGS The famous French dish which is highly thought of as an aphrodisiac. The interest in frogs as an amatory aid goes back to the Roman times when many a good orgy got underway with the help of a frog or two.

G

GALANGA A root found in India which can be powdered down and used in various concoctions. Often mixed with aromatic seeds such as **CARDAMOMS** or **CLOVES**. Very popular in Arab countries and goes back to the Middle Ages.

GALANTINE A concoction of white meat which is specially treated with herbs and spices and eaten cold. Said to have a dynamic effect on the amatory urges.

GARLIC This plant is commonly used in cooking because of its strong smell and taste. It has a great reputation for promoting good health as it has a built-in resistance to poison. It increases the staying power in intercourse and thus heightens and prolongs the pleasure for both parties.

GENTIAN A rare plant which sometimes sprouts blue flowers. One of the oldest aphrodisiacs, which brings fervour and zeal to any act of love. An erotic wine can be made from the roots of the plant which was favoured by the lusty Romans.

GHEE The Indian term for clarified butter. This is used

extensively in Indian cookery and is firmly hailed as a love-provoker.

GILLYFLOWER A plant which is used in cooking because of its strong flavouring properties resembling the clove's. It is often an ingredient in love potions and has a great reputation for awakening hidden desires. Sometimes known as JULY-FLOWERS, and a member of the same family as the wallflower.

GINGER This hot root is renowned for its strengthening properties, and can be relied upon to make the union between man and woman hot, spicy and strong. It can be used in cooking, and in baking, e.g. gingerbread, and in drinks, e.g. ginger beer (which is a most effective way to take the root for quick results).

GIN SENG This is an ancient Chinese aphrodisiac which was believed to prolong a youthful and active sex life. In China, women over sixty years of age have been known to give birth to healthy and happy babies after they have taken gin seng over a period. Marco Polo found it was in use all over China in 1274. Because it is a root it is easy to use in almost any food or drink, and always it brings erotic feelings and enhances the sex drive. In the Sik-Hote-Alin mountains, the Russians have opened several experimental stations to analyse the effects of gin seng. They are growing the root in large quantities. It is especially good as an energy-giving substance.

GLUCOSE Also known as 'dextrose'. This is grape sugar and is widely used as a sweetener, guaranteed to give enough stamina to sweeten any relationship.

GOAT'S EYE This furry-looking ring is an age-old cunning device worn on the penis by Arabs to enable them to cope with the demands of the harem. It brings on a climax with great speed, and thus saves time so that the rest of the queue can be serviced.

GOAT SUET This goes back to Elizabethan times when it was a regular practice to annoint the penis with suet made from the goat. This apparently has such a profound effect on the man's sexual performance that once the woman got a taste of that kind of love-making it was considered certain that she would stay forever faithful. One important point was that the suet had to be made from the middle-sized goat only. Not the big goat and not the small one.

GONADS These deliver the internal secretions to the blood. Sexual emotion depends upon a good supply of nutrients. People on starvation diets in concentration camps quickly lose interest in sex because of lack of protein. In the mating season some animals are given extra protein foods to increase sexual drive.

GOOSE Mainly of interest for the goose liver which is believed to be one of the most famous and potent of all aphrodisiacs. In some countries, the goose is the symbol of potency.

GOPALIKA A plant which can be powdered down and used in a concoction of various herbs and spices as an amatory aid.

GOSSYPION In mediaeval times the juice extracted from the gossypion tree was a well-known and effective love potion.

GOULASH A Hungarian dish made from beef, vegetables and PAPRIKA, the extra hot Hungarian pepper, which heats the body until it burns with desire.

GOUROU This is the African word for 'kola-nut' which is a large sharp-tasting nutritious nut. The essence is used in the making of the popular cola drink which is known to refresh and invigorate the senses. See KOLA.

GRAPES These are accepted as being an aphrodisiac partly because they are the fruit that wine comes from, and partly because of the shape of the grape. The juice of the grape is a tried and trusted love potion.

GREEN PEPPER The hot plant which can put fire into an affair.

GUDUCHI A plant found in India which has a reputation for enflaming the passions. In Hindu practice it is pounded down and mixed with milk, honey, GHEE, and other plant powders to form a strong love philtre.

H

HADDOCK Often looked upon as an aphrodisiac because of the association between fish, the sea, and Aphrodite, the goddess who rose from the sea.

HAGGIS This most nutritious food is powerful in its sustaining properties and by its nature and shape is an obvious aphrodisiac.

HALIBUT This can have sex-strengthening power on two accounts. It can be taken as a meal, or the oil of the fish can be extracted and used in food to give stimulating results.

HAM This common food rich in Vitamin E is in fact the thigh of the hog which has been dried and salted. There are many ways of serving this dish, and two favourite accompanying foods are CABBAGE and PINEAPPLE both of which are aphrodisiacs.

HARE This is believed to be an aphrodisiac, probably because most wild game comes under this heading. The hare is noted for speed and will bring lightning flashes to an affair.

HARICOT BEANS These are French beans high in protein value and believed to increase desire.

HARMINE A very dangerous drug which can produce erotic hallucinations, but also affects the brain. It is obtained from the leaves of the plant BANISTERIA CAAPI found in South America, and also from the seeds of WILD RUE which is found in Australia.

HASHISH This is the term given to INDIAN HEMP, a plant used in the making of rope. Hashish has a strong intoxicating effect which can lead to amorous inclinations. There is the danger of becoming addicted to this potent drug.

HAZELNUT Nuts come under the heading of nature's pure foods, and when taken pure and untampered with, they serve the body with good supplies of necessary protein. As well as being good for the body, the general idea conjured up in the mind in connection with nuts is one of a comparison to the male testicles.

HEDYSARUM GANGETICUM A plant found in India, the leaves of which can be powdered down to form an ingredient of a potent love drink called SANSEVIERA.

HELEBORE A plant which was used extensively for medicinal purposes. At one time it was administered to patients as a cure for madness. In Arab countries it was one of the ingredients in a love brew consisting of various herbs and spices thought to cure impotency.

HENNA The leaves of this plant have been used for centuries as a hair dye. The Arabs look upon it as a sex aid and they use it as a balsam because if its thick creamy texture.

AUBREY
BEARDSLEY.

HERISSAH An oriental dish consisting mainly of mutton and pepper, and looked upon as a sexual stimulant.

HERMITAGE A drink reputed to have strong sex-provoking tendencies. This belief was widely held in the eighteenth century.

HERRING Because of the association with the sea, this is known for having aphrodisiac qualities.

HIPPOCRAS The name given to the traditional love potion made from red wine mixed with ginger, cloves, vanilla, cinnamon and sugar.

HOMINY GRITS This is an American breakfast cereal made from maize which has been hulled, ground and boiled. It contains Vitamin E which is vital for a good sex performance.

HONEY The golden love potion of the gods, famous through the ages for inducing love-making. One of nature's kindest healers. Honey can heal open wounds, eliminate the pain of a burn, act as a beautifier when applied directly on to the face, and above all, it keeps the inner self happy, healthy and ripe for sensual excitement.

HORSERADISH This plant has such a piercing pungent root that it is looked upon as setting the heart on fire as well as the emotions. It was considered that the only way to extinguish the flame was to indulge in the most passionate of love-making.

HOT DOG In addition to the phallic shape influence on the mind, the hot dog also has the element of heat which adds a further dimension to its attractions as an aphrodisiac.

HYDROCOTYLE This is a plant found in marshy land, bogs or by the edge of a stream. It is widely used in China, and in fact one well-known Chinese herbalist called Chang-Li-Yun who was in the habit of taking hydrocotyle lived to the age of 256. He died in the year 1933 by which time he had been married twenty-four times.

HYDROMEL The name given to a mixture of honey and water which was believed to be a love potion.

HYPOMANE The Romans are believed to have brewed this highly powerful beverage made up of the secretions from the reproductive organs of colts and mares, mixed with herbs. It is believed to give stallion-like stamina in sex performance.

HYSSOP A small aromatic herb which is believed to give a sexual flavour when added to any food or drink.

VENUS.

I

INDIAN HEMP This is the plant from which the drug hashish comes. See HASHISH.

INOSITOL This is not in itself an aphrodisiac, but it is worth mentioning because it is the vitamin which is essential for the healthy functioning of the liver. It prevents premature ageing, and is responsible for keeping us young in mind and body and full of the joys and love of life.

IODINE Although strictly speaking, iodine in itself is not an aphrodisiac, it does have some bearing on the inclination and ability to make love and to enjoy it. This is because iodine is necessary to keep the THYROID gland operating in a healthy manner. The thyroid gives off a secretion which has an influence on the sexual drive and in order to live a wholesome active sex life it is imperative to have sufficient supplies of iodine.

IRON It is essential to have good supplies of iron in the body in order to keep the blood healthy and therefore the whole body in a fit state conducive to the natural sexual drive. Pregnant women are given vast amounts of iron tablets in order to replenish the iron which is taken from their blood by the unborn child. Iron can be taken in many forms including tablets, capsules, liquid, and by an injection straight into the blood-stream. A food which is rich in iron is LIVER.

ISINGLASS This is a jelly-type of substance which is got from fish and in particular the STURGEON – the caviare fish. The jelly has a two-fold reason for evoking the passions. Firstly there is the nature of the substance which closely relates to the sexual secretions, and secondly there is the connection with the sea through the fish and therefore the association with Aphrodite.

ITERISI A herb sometimes known as PROVINCIA which was very popular as an aphrodisiac in the thirteenth century. It was mixed with food and drinks for the best effects.

J

JASMINE This is a flowering shrub that gives off a delightful perfume. It is worn in the East by women who are out to hunt down and capture the male species – at least certain 'members' of it.

JEFFRIES Graham H. Jeffries MB., Ch.B., who writes for the *New England Journal of Medicine* is involved in the unravelling of the mysteries of Vitamin B12. This is the vitamin given to patients suffering from infertility caused by a blood condition called 'pernicious anaemia'. When such patients are treated with B12, there is invariably an amazing change in their sex life due to a more rewarding and fruitful performance.

JUICE OF CELERY The juice extracted from the fleshy CELERY stem can be used in various ways. It can be added to soups, stews and casserole dishes, it can be added to fruit drinks and cocktails, or it can be taken as a straight health drink. The celery stick is an aphrodisiac and for those who dislike the taste of the whole shoot a good alternative would be to take the juice only, as in this way it is easy to camouflage the taste and at the same time retain the entrancing qualities that lead to sexual stimulation.

JULEP A drink often served with mint and believed to refresh and excite the body into a state ripe for love. Often used for medicinal purposes.

JULIENNE A type of clear soup to which various stimulants can be added to promote a heightened sexual awareness.

JULY-FLOWERS Another name for GILLYFLOWER which is a clove-scented plant used in amatory connections.

JUNIPER A shrub of the evergreen variety which bears bitter purple berries from which is extracted a very special oil – the oil of juniper. This has an unusually delicate aura surrounding it and is widely used for medicinal purposes. The main ingredient of gin, this strange mystifying oil can set the senses reeling.

K

KAHAWAI A large salmon-type fish found in the sea surrounding New Zealand and believed to be a strong aphrodisiac. Used in Maori feasts to promote amatory adventures.

KAMA SUTRA The famous book, the *Kama Sutra* which has fired the imagination of thousands of people all over the world has added a new dimension to the lives and loves of all who follow its golden rules. It recommends a special recipe for sex which is guaranteed to excite the body to an uncontrollable state of lust. The ingredients are as follows:

Take some butter which has been made from buffalo milk and melt it down until it takes a liquid form. This substance is called GHEE. Mix this liquid with ordinary cow's milk. Then melt some black treacle and gently stir the melted treacle into the mixture of milk and ghee. Boil a portion of ASPARAGUS until tender, then add some spices of your choice, such as cinnamon or ginger, taking care to blend them well into the mixture. Finally melt down some LIQUORICE and blend into the brew. Anyone who indulges in this dish can look forward to mounting passions and a total awakening of hitherto hidden desires.

KARENGRO A plant similar in appearance to an ORCHID. A favourite aphrodisiac in European gypsy camps where it is believed to enhance a sexual union.

KASURIKA A plant found in India the fruits of which form part of the ingredients of a potent Hindu love philtre.

KAVA The romatic South Sea Islanders enjoy this drink which is made from a Polynesian plant of the pepper family. It coaxes and stirs the emotions until they are ripe and eager for the pleasures of the flesh.

KEDGEREE The ingredients of this dish make it a sure-fire method of enflaming the soul. Fish from the sea and eggs, both strong aphrodisiacs in their own right.

KEITAFO BANLON This is taken in the form of tablets which are made in Hong Kong and exported to England and the Continent. It is commonly known as the VIRILITY PILL as it stimulates passion and promotes the animal urge that lies deep within all human beings. The tablets have undergone extensive laboratory tests and have been passed as being harmless with no side-effects.

KELP A large weed found in the sea. When this is burnt its ashes yield that most important substance, IODINE, which is so essential for the thyroid gland in order to stay sexually healthy and aware.

KIDNEY BEAN A small French bean of the runner type which can make the emotions run riot.

KIDNEYS & CREAM This unlikely-sounding concoction is said to have hidden powers beyond ordinary understanding. The kidneys supply the vital energy needed to sustain the body during the long hours of constant sexual ardour which can be expected to follow the consuming of this dish. The cream acts as food for the imagination and in this combination with the kidneys, it lights the way to previously unexplored realms of the sex jungle.

KIPPER Here we have the double effect of the fish and the salt. The fish of the sea with its association with Aphrodite and the salt of the earth. This combination produces a delightful stimulant of base earthy lust and fanciful flights of desire.

KNICKERBOCKER GLORY The lush ingredients of fruits (for virility) and cream, coupled with the word-association of 'knickers' and the female sex parts have a titillating effect on the mind.

KOLA The nuts of the kola tree, found in Africa, are the main ingredient of the highly commercialised drink sold the world over. There are certain stimulating properties in the nut which also goes into the making of chocolate. The African natives chew the nut which has an exciting effect upon the nerve ends.

KSHIRIKA An Oriental plant resembling an onion in appearance, which is popular for its juice which is believed to be an effective love potion.

KUILI A powder which can be mixed with milk and various vegetables such as asparagus and cucumber to form a stimulating love potion. Highly thought of in India.

KUMMEL A liqueur made popular in Germany which is made from CUMIN. It has the power to create a dizzy craving for sensual indulgence.

KYPHI A paste which if applied directly onto the body produces heightened sensitivity. The ancient Egyptians used it as a sex ointment.

LYSISTRATA.

L

LAMB This food is very rich in vitamin B2 and can have amazing effects, especially when it is served with mint sauce, as MINT is an aphrodisiac in its own right.

LAMPREY A fish which resembles an eel in appearance and is believed to promote conception due to an increase in the amount of sperm released during love-making.

LARD Being a substance formed from animal fat, this has a suggestive influence in the mind connected with animals, lust and earthy feeling. An erotic cream can be made by mixing lard with garlic and aromatic herbs.

LAUREL A shrub, the glossy leaves of which at one time were used in love play, especially in the Orient where they were noted for 'sitting on their laurels'.

LAVENDER Used for centuries as a perfume, lavender can also be smoked. A mixture of only a few flowers with tobacco is capable of producing a pleasant sexy trance.

LECITHIN A substance which is part of the make-up of various foods and is believed to stimulate the sex glands.

LENTIL This is the edible seed of a leguminous or pod-bearing plant. They are popular in India and are widely used in Indian soups and curried meals.

LIBIDO This is the ability to have intercourse. To maintain a healthy libido it is essential to keep in the right frame of mind and have the correct attitude towards the sexual act. Fatigue and nervous tension are both bitter obstacles to attaining a vigorous sex life, therefore great care should be taken to ensure that the best possible foods are taken to keep the entire body fit and full of energy.

LION In mediaeval times, lions were looked upon as a symbol of virility. The fat of a lion was believed to increase sexual prowess if rubbed into the genitals.

LIQUORICE A plant from the root of which a black substance is obtained which is widely used in medicine and cookery. In some countries, particularly India, it is used in love potions.

LIVER The liver of the cow is well known for its aphrodisiac qualities and it is also a most nutritious dish giving a long list of benefits to both the body and the mind. The Romans used dried liver mixed with various drinks as a love potion.

LIZARD In Arab countries the lizard is believed to induce a longing for sex-play if held in the hand. It is sometimes eaten in powdered form and is reputed to play havoc with the desires.

LOBSTER The lobster is looked upon as a great delicacy and together with the sea-connections and the red appearance when boiled it can spark off a series of mental gymnastics which can only be tamed by indulging in hot frenzied sex.

LOTUS FLOWER In the Orient it is believed that if the pollen from the lotus flower is mixed with honey then applied to the penis, it guarantees improved performance.

LYCOPODIUM A plant which is reputed to stimulate desire. The root can be chopped and added to various dishes as a forerunner to sex play.

M

MACKEREL This sea fish with the blue and silver stripes can reach deep into the heart and soul and shake the senses into a whirling sea of sexual excitement.

MADAYANTAKA A plant which is popular because of the juice which is obtained from its roots. This is used in a Hindu love potion along with various other ingredients to increase the sexual appetite.

MADEIRA A rich wine of the sherry variety which comes from the island of Madeira. It warms the blood and stimulates the senses. A particularly fine sponge-type cake called 'Madeira cake' is made with this sherry and eggs and with this combination, has obvious aphrodisiac attractions.

MAERUA ARENARIA An Indian herb which has reputation for prolonging staying power during sexual intercourse.

MA-FU-SHUAN A narcotic found in China and believed to have strong aphrodisiac tendencies. Was very popular in the seventeenth century.

MAIDENHAIR A herb which is not surprisingly believed to be an aphrodisiac.

MAIZE Found in India this corn grows as high as six feet, and is also grown in great quantities in America.

MALLOW A wild purple-flowered plant which oozes a sap believed to have powerful love-evoking qualities, especially if mixed with goat's milk. Very popular in Roman times.

MANDRAKE Properly known as *Madragora Autumnaus,* this is one of the oldest and best known aphrodisiacs. The thick mandrake root divides in two and closely resembles in appearance the thighs of a man. When the root is pulled up from the ground it makes the strangest shrieking sound. It was widely used in biblical times and is even quoted in the book of Genesis XXX 14 – 16, where it is recorded that Leah employed the help of the mandrake root in her escapades with the promiscuous Jacob. There is no doubt as to the results of her labours, because exactly nine months after their amorous encounter, Leah gave birth to an illegitimate child.

MANGO A tropical fruit which is looked upon as an aphrodisiac because of its appearance, also on account of the oil which can be extracted and rubbed directly onto the genitals. This is believed to increase the sexual desire.

MARIJUANA This powerful drug has the effect of depressing the inhibitive centres of the mind and body, therefore allowing a free flow of emotions and urges. Its proper name is *Cannabis Sativa.* At the moment there is a big controversy as to whether or not this drug should be made legal. See CANNABIS.

MARJORAM A herb which is looked upon as a love stimulant, often eaten in salads. The fresh leaves have antibiotic properties. The tea which can be made from this herb stimulates the circulation of the blood and gives an appetite for sensual pleasures.

MARROW This large fleshy vegetable has become a standing joke with comics because of its resemblance to a giant penis, and is an automatic choice for 'aphrodisiac of the year'.

MARZIPAN A widely-used confection made of powdered almonds and sugar, believed to encourage lust.

MASTIC A pale yellow gum resin which is obtained from the mastic tree and highly favoured as a love aid by the Arabs.

MASTURBATION The hand in the service of the imagination, *and* you don't have to look your best!

MATELOTE A sauce especially suited to fish dishes. It is made up from the following ingredients: onions, parsley, cloves clarets and vinegar. The stew of the fish can also be added to make this a highly potent aphrodisiac due to the fact that the two main ingredients are the wine and the fish. The latter with its sea association and the former with its intoxicating properties.

MEAD This is a very 'old world' drink and has a strong effect on the sensations. It is a mixture of alcohol and HONEY that can spin the head, and lower resistance to amorous advances, allowing the act of love to take on a more vigorous nature.

MEADOW-SWEET The sweet-smelling plant with white flowers, believed to be a love token which brings joy to lovers who carry the blossom while indulging in amatory practices.

MEAT All red meat and in particular lean meat has long been looked upon as a strong aphrodisiac. Especially effective if taken with hearty red wine.

MELON A kind of gourd, i.e. a large fleshy fruit from a trailing or climbing plant. Usually the rind of such fruits can be used as a vessel. The association between melons and female breasts makes this a most provocative food causing men to lust after the women of their choice.

MESCALINE A dangerous drug which is obtained from a type of cactus called *peyote,* found in Mexico and Texas. The small button-like growth of the plant is dried and can be consumed in various ways, including in liquid form. It produces sexual sensations but also horrific hallucinations. This drug should not be taken without medical supervision.

MILK The milk of various animals such as the ass and the goat is reputed to possess aphrodisiac properties. Cleopatra was said to have bathed in milk, as was the wife of the Roman Emperor Nero. This practice was believed to enhance sexual attraction.

MINT An aromatic plant which is used to add an interesting flavour to many otherwise uninteresting dishes. The famous mint sauce is usually served with LAMB. Many health drinks and cocktails are improved by adding a touch of mint, giving them exuberance and zest.

AVBREY BEARDSLEY.

MOH A tree found in India bearing flowers from which the spirit ARRACK is obtained. The bark of the tree can be pounded and mixed with milk to produce a love philtre, popular in Hindu circles.

MOLASSES This is the drainings or treacle that is got from raw sugar and is a great source of energy. The body gets the strength needed for sustained heavy love-making.

MOLY A plant reputed to have strong sexual powers. It is believed that it is related to WILD RUE which is an evergreen found in Australia from which the drug HARMINE is obtained.

MUGWORT An Oriental plant which is reputed to possess stimulating properties of a sexual nature.

MULBERRY A purple fruit believed to stir up sexual sensations. The leaves of the mulberry bush are used extensively in silk-worm feeding.

MULTIVITE This is a term given to a tablet or capsule containing all or most of the vitamins. Multivitamin tablets can be got at chemists and these are a good way of ensuring that the body gets all the vitamins required for a healthy and happy life, rich in the joys of sexual bliss.

MUOC-MAN A mixture popular in China, made from rotted fish and garlic, among other things. When added to food it is believed to stir up sexual excitement.

MUSCAT This is the name given to a certain type of grape which has a peculiar musk flavour. The strong wine which is made from these grapes is known to make the senses reel.

MUSHROOM The mushroom goes through six stages of opening out to become the fully-fledged umbrella shape that we think of as the mature mushroom. In one of its early stages it is called the 'button'. This is when the head is still fairly closed up and almost circular in shape. At this point it can be compared with the shape of the penis.

MUSK This is the secretion obtained from a gland of the musk deer. Various plants have an aroma reminiscent of musk and are extensively used in the perfume business. It has a heavy sultry smell with sexual overtones.

MUSSÈL A shellfish with a double shell, associated with Aphrodite. This seafood can lead to an inflamed sexual urge.

MUSTARD The mustard seed is ground down to make a fine powder, and this is then made into a paste. This is used as a condiment. The most famous mustards are French, American and English. Because of the strong heating agent, mustard is believed to fire the imagination to attain great heights of passion. It is a very rich food, high in Vitamin E, the sex vitamin.

MUTTON The flesh of a fully-grown sheep which is eaten in meat form or used to make a tasty soup. Through the years this food has been hailed as a love-monger capable of breaking down the most ice-cold barriers of human inhibitions. Especially popular in Arab countries where it is eaten with caraway seeds.

MYOSOTIS A small plant with tiny blue flowers long associated with amorous encounters. The plant is commonly called 'Forget-me-not'.

MYROBALAN A fruit similar in appearance to the PLUM and used by the Romans as a love-inspiring food, prominent at their many and celebrated sex orgies.

MYRRH An aromatic gum found in the Orient and highly thought of as a love stimulant by Arabs. Also used for medicinal purposes.

MYRTLE An evergreen shrub which is believed to promote sexual feelings and lead to a fulfilment of desire. A love philtre can be made by mixing the flowers of myrtle with white wine.

N

NAVELWORT Tradition has it that this herb possesses strange alluring properties and can be trusted to inspire a loved one to display the depth of his or her passion.

NECTAR The substance obtained from flowers which goes into the making of honey. Reputed to be the drink of the gods, and used in amatory potions.

NECTARINE A type of PEACH which is well-endowed with aphrodisiac qualities.

NEDDE A concoction of various aromatic substances including amber which is used as a love ointment in Arab countries.

NEGUS A hot potent drink made from wine and water which combines the water/sea thought-suggestion with Aphrodite and the intoxicating properties of the wine made extra potent when heated.

NEPENTHE A drug which is administered in order to banish grief. If taken in a mixture of wine, it can have the effect of breaking down inhibitions and promoting amorous incidents.

NETTLES The oil which can be extracted from nettles was used by the Romans as a lubricant which was believed to help attain a better sexual performance. It was also their custom to whip their genitals with the stinging nettle leaves in order to put some sting into their sexual adventures and to provoke their women into accommodating their desires.

NIACIN The substance which is found in yeast, liver, kidney, milk and wholegrain products, necessary for a healthy beautiful skin and attraction to the opposite sex.

NICEROTIANA An exotic perfume used by the Romans to increase amatory inclinations.

NINJIN A root found in Japan and believed to be an extremely effective love tonic.

NUT All nuts are said to have aphrodisiac qualities, partly because of their high protein yield (thus giving vitality and stamina), and partly because of the shape which can be compared with the male sexual organs. This applies especially to the larger variety such as walnuts, chestnuts, brazils, etc.

NUTMEG Found in India, this comes from the seed of a tree and is strongly aromatic with powerful narcotic tendencies. Nutmeg should be used with great care allowing only a small amount at a time as it is a vigorous sexual persuader.

NYMPHAEA An Indian tree, the leaves of which can be powdered down, mixed with various plants and herbs and smeared over the sexual organs to ensure virility.

O

OATMEAL Famous for its strength-giving properties, oatmeal is rich in Vitamin E, the love vitamin. Also, when applied to the face, it acts as a beauty mask.

OCTOPUS The sea-association of the octopus lists it among the numbers of aphrodisiacs – also the eight arms carry a thought-suggestion to the mind of multiple embraces and greatly increased sexual participation.

OIL Oils of various types are used as body lubricants, and due to the comparison between this substance and sexual secretions it has the power to initiate the love urge.

OINTMENT Both the texture and perfume of many ointments result in them being looked upon as aphrodisiacs. Also when ointment is applied to the body, the 'rubbing-in' has the effect of stimulating the body and arousing the desires.

OLIBANUM An aromatic resin which the Arabs mix with nutmeg and honey to produce staggering sexual results.

OLIVE The olive has the name for bringing peace and harmony, and being an evergreen it suggests that lovers will live in love and understanding of each other for ever. The oil which can be extracted from the olive is extensively used for medicinal and culinary purposes.

OLOLUIGUI A substance obtained from *Rivea Corynbosa*, which is a plant found in the tropics. There is a connection with MESCALINE, the dangerous drug which produces hallucinations and sexual tendencies.

ONION Because of their bulbous appearance, onions have always been among the top aphrodisiacs and are used the world over for their flavouring properties. Believed to add pep and flavour to the act of love. The Greeks had great faith in a mixture of white onions and green vegetables which are rich in Vitamin E.

OPIUM The dangerous drug obtained from poppies which produces hallucinations of a sexual nature.

ORANGE Nell Gwynne, the famous peasant orange pedlar, and mistress of King Charles, was responsible for the orange aphrodisiac association. As was the style of the times, she was in the habit of wearing very low-cut revealing necklines and thus initiated the comparison between the orange and the female breasts.

ORCHID There are many varieties of the orchid flower which is regarded as the flower for romance. A special drink called 'salep' is made from the juices of certain orchids which are said to have magical love-potion characteristics. In Greek the word means 'testes', which bears out the resemblance of this flower to the male genitals.

ORCHIS HIRCINA The plant, the roots of which are hailed as the famous aphrodisiac SATYRION.

ORRIS This plant comes from the iris family and has a root which gives off a perfume similar to that of the violet. The scent can reach deep within until it stirs and provokes the sexual juices to flow.

OTTO This is the name given to an exclusive oil which is made from the petals of the rose, which is the greatest love token of our age. When the oil is applied it ensures that the bond between the lovers will enclose them in a circle of everlasting devotion.

OYSTER Sometimes looked upon as being similar in shape to the female genitals. This together with the sea-connection gives them an exciting aura.

P

PAPAW A tree which bears fruit similar in shape to the melon which automatically connects it with female breasts. The juice of this fruit is well known to be an aid to digestion.

PAPRIKA This extra hot Hungarian red pepper must only be given in small amounts for the best effect, and to bring any love affair to a sizzling point. One of the most famous dishes made from paprika pepper is GOULASH.

PARSLEY Widely used for seasoning, this herb can add that 'extra something' to any dish, and in consequence, it will also add something extra to enhance any sexual partnership.

PARSNIP A hot vegetable which enflames the imagination and has a second aphrodisiac attraction in the fact that it is phallus-shaped.

PARTRIDGE Another example of the wild game bird which conjures up visions of loose women and willing sex participants.

PEA It is not clear exactly why peas seem to hold a certain aphrodisiac quality, but the fact is that they tend to possess strange powers that provoke and awake sexual feelings. They contain Vitamin B2.

PEACH The shape of the peach contributes to its powers as a sex stimulant being not unlike the female buttocks. This fruit transmits pleasant thoughts to the mind of attractive and beautiful things, hence the saying 'a peach of a girl' and when referring to a beautiful clear skin, 'a complexion like peaches and cream'. Peaches are famous for sense, touch and smell, all necessary for a successful love life.

PEANUT Universally accepted to be rich in protein and the stuff that makes for passionate love play, reminiscent of the jungle.

PEAR The striking resemblance between pears and female breasts explains the attraction of this fruit as an aphrodisiac.

PELLITORY The common name for the PYRETHRUM plant, or as known by its botanical name – *Pyrethrum Parthenium*. This plant was pounded down and mixed with ginger and lilac essence to form an exotic ointment prized by the Arabs who believed that if the genitals were annointed with this mixture then the sex drive would become rampant. This plant was also popular as a sexual appetiser, served before orgies.

PENNYROYAL This is an aromatic herb of the MINT family and possesses all of the aphrodisiac qualities of the mint.

PEPPER There are many types of peppers and generally speaking the red variety are the hottest. All pepper heats the senses and they have the name of being responsible for enflaming the pulses with lust.

PEPPERMINT The thought-connections between the hot pepper and the pungent mint play tricks on the mind and produce extreme carnal sensations.

PERFUME One of the best-known wiles of women to allure the men of their choice into the pleasures of love and romance.

PERIWINKLE A small edible shellfish which has an effect on the emotions due to its association with the sea and Aphrodite.

PERRY Pears are the main ingredient of this drink and therefore there is the double attraction of pears being akin to the female breasts, and the intoxicating effect of the alcoholic content. See PEAR.

PHEASANT The bright plumage makes this game bird a most eye-catching sight. It has the reputation for evoking frivolous and giddy feelings, ready for fun. The saying 'she's a game bird' could well have originated from the pheasant.

PHILTRE This is the technical term given to a love potion.

PIGEON As well as being a game bird, which is recommendation enough in itself, the pigeon has always had romantic associations connected with being a carrier of messages, in particular love letters. At the sight of the homing pigeon, a lover would feel the excitement and anticipation of the bond of love.

PIKE Although this is in fact a freshwater fish there still remains the thought-association between fish and sea, and sea and Aphrodite. Love and passion knows no barriers.

PIMENTO A type of ALLSPICE which by its hot pepper characteristic is listed among the foods which have powers to stimulate the sex organs. In the twelfth century Peter the Venerable forbade his monks to eat pimentos because of the provocative effect they caused in the genital regions.

PIMPINELLA ANISUM More commonly known as 'anise', a plant from which aromatic seeds are obtained. These are widely used for flavouring purposes. The liqueur 'anisette' is prepared from ANISEED. In mediaeval times, anise was highly regarded as an aphrodisiac.

PINE The fresh aroma of this evergreen refreshes the mind and body and coaxes the spirit into a mood ripe for love-making. The shape of the pine cone is phallic and this adds to the attraction.

PINEAPPLE When served with sugar, pineapples become a food with strong entrancing qualities acting as a love balm on the senses.

AVBREY
BEARDSLEY

PISTACHIO This is the name given to the nut of the turpentine tree which contains a most pleasant-tasting kernel and being of the nut family has the ability to excite and arouse the passions.

PIZZA URURDU An Italian plant which is believed to be a very strong sex aid and is used in cases of frigidity.

PLAICE Together with PIKE this fish has an aphrodisiac attraction due to its sea-connection and can bring the effect of vigorous sexual love activity.

PLANTAIN A banana-like fruit which is found in the tropics and is an obvious aphrodisiac due to its phallic shape.

PLUM The plumpness and shape of the plum is in some eyes comparative to the testicles and this leads to excitement and arousal of the sexual organs.

POCULUM AMATORIUM The name given to a famous love potion popular with the Romans. The name means 'love cup' which was a mixture of aphrodisiac herbs and spices.

POMADE A scented ointment which when worn on the hair is said to have magnetic attraction for the opposite sex.

POMEGRANATE This delightful fruit owes its aphrodisiac qualities to the fact that it is filled with seeds and they suggest thoughts of reproduction to the mind. Highly favoured by the Romans.

POONAC After the oil has been extracted from the coconut, the substance that remains is called 'poonac', and because of the nut association to the male sexual organs, this poonac is believed to also have aphrodisiac properties in its own right.

PORT Often called the drink of love, port wine is a strong red drink which is said to possess qualities to coax the coldest-hearted into a warm and loving sex partner.

POTATO As far back as the days of Shakespeare, potatoes were looked upon as producing bodily lust. In his famous work *The Merry Wives of Windsor*, Shakespeare refers to the potato as an aphrodisiac.

POTEEN This is the name given to a raw drink of Irish whiskey which has been illicitly brewed. Sometimes it is served before the complete fermenting process has been allowed to take place. It can blow the mind and allow the passions to run riot.

PRAWN Another example of a food being aphrodisiac because of its connections with the sea.

PROSTATE GLAND The male sexual organ where sperm is secreted. If this gland is enlarged it produces a weak bladder, and possible impotency. An age-old cure for this trouble is to feed on PUMPKIN SEED as they preserve the prostate gland.

PROTEIN Necessary for the stimulation of the sex glands, protein can be obtained from the following foods: meat, eggs, fish, cheese and milk.

[87]

PROVINCIA A herb which was believed to be a strong aphrodisiac which excited men and women alike. Popular in the thirteenth century. Sometimes known as ITERISI.

PRUNE So strong was the belief in prunes, which are of course dried plums, as an aphrodisiac in the Elizabethan times that they were often served in brothels free of charge. By their shape and nature they conjured up visions of testicles and sex organs and excited the customers to such a pitch that it was necessary for the ladies to spend only the minimum amount of time on each client before they reached a satisfying climax. In this way they were able to fit in more customers, and therefore the brothel owner made more money, faster.

PRUNELLE DE BOURGOGNE A liqueur made from the juice of prunes which entices the emotions along the pathway leading to love.

PUMPKIN SEED Both the pumpkin and the seeds are said to have powers to turn the mind and body to matters of love. The seeds represent the reproductive element of the sex act and the pumpkin can be compared with the female breasts. The pumpkin has a good supply of Vitamin B2.

PUNCH Because of the very nature of this drink it is one of the aphrodisiacs that seldom fail. The combination of various intoxicating alcoholic drinks together with fruit, herbs and spices leads the passions to a dizzy frenzy and leaves a consuming thirst for fast, satisfying sex.

PYRETHRUM Properly known as *Pyrethrum Parthenium*. This plant was used by the Arabs as an ointment after it had been pounded and mixed with ginger and lilac essence. It was massaged into the genitals and was believed to produce a vigorous sex drive. It is sometimes known as PELLITORY.

Q

QUAIL This is a small bird of the PARTRIDGE family and is looked upon as an aphrodisiac because of the game association in the mind.

QUASSIA A tree which grows in the jungles of South America. The wood and bark of the tree are used in the making of a special tonic drink which spurs the senses on towards a tumult of sexual expression.

QUEEN APPLE The popular name given to a French apple called 'rennet' which in typical French fashion can sweep the senses into a wave of ecstasy.

QUICKSILVER Another name for mercury, the speed metal. Quicksilver is the substance used in the Japanese sex gadget called a WATAMA which speedily brings erotic joy to any woman wearing it.

QUINCE This is a fruit very similar to the pear in shape but rather than the juice being sweet as in the case of the pear, the quince fruit has a somewhat acid taste. Its shape resembles the female breasts. It can be made into a jelly and used as an external amatory aid.

QUININE A famous cure for fever, this bitter drug which is made from the bark of a tree can be made into a potent drink which is both a health tonic and sex stimulant. Very popular in Persia and often taken just before a night of love.

QUITCH Otherwise known as 'quitch-grass', 'dog-grass', or 'couch-grass', this widespread weed acts as a carpet of nature, and lovers enjoy its inviting texture.

R

RABBIT PIE A pleasant way of serving rabbit which is an aphrodisiac due to the sexual habits of this creature, having the reputation for fast and furious reproduction.

RADISH The bitter-tasting radish is among the hot foods with aphrodisiac powers to hot up any love affair. Very popular in Germany and France.

RADIX CHINAE An ancient aphrodisiac in which great faith was placed right up to mediaeval times.

RAKTA-BOL An aromatic substance otherewise known as **MYRRH** which is believed to have powerful love-inducing qualities. A paste can be made by mixing *rakta-bol* with other aromatic herbs and gums. In Hindu tradition, if this paste is rubbed into the sexual parts, then the love-making will take on a more vigorous and prolonged nature.

RASPBERRY The small, soft, red and plump raspberry has mind-associations with female nipples.

RAUWILOID A drug which is extracted from the root of the plant *Rauwolfia Serpentina*, found in Asia and South America. It is sometimes known as 'reserpine'. Widely used in India as a medicine and believed to have some aphrodisiac qualities it is especially noted for causing dreams of an erotic nature. The plant was named after the sixteenth-century German horticulturist Leonhard Rauwolf. The roots resemble a snake hence the tag *Serpentina*. In India the dried roots are commonly chewed as an aid to concentration. Many monks and holy men indulge in this practice during meditation hours.

RED PEPPER Of all the various types of peppers, the red variety is by far the hottest, assured to send hot tingles down the spine.

RED SANDERS A substance which also comes in a yellow form. Very popular in mediaeval times as a sex stimulant when added to food and drinks. Properly known as *Pterocarpus Santalinus*. See also YELLOW SANDERS.

RHUBARB Because of the long phallic shape of the rhubarb stick it is looked upon as an aphrodisiac and in fact is used both internally and externally for sexual fulfilment.

RIBOFLAVIN Vitamin B2, essential for general well-being and good health. This vitamin gives good strong shining hair, a healthy mouth and clear bright eyes. It helps to maintain a pleasing and attractive appearance which is enticing to the opposite sex.

RICE The cereal plant grown extensively in the East and believed to be an aphrodisiac, possibly due to the fact that it is often served with other accepted aphrodisiacs such as meat, eggs, fish, etc. A Hindu love meal consists of rice mixed with honey and ghee.

RICE OIL The name given to a yellow oily substance obtained from the leaves of the *Ruta Graveolens* plant. This is a strong aphrodisiac and has been compared with CANTHARIDES in its effect upon the genitals.

ROCKET The name given to a type of cabbage found in the Mediterranean countries and used as part of a salad dish. It was boiled as a powerful method of increasing lust as far back as Roman times. Properly known as BRASSICA ERUCA.

ROE The mass of eggs from a fish, having the double aphrodisiac effect from both the eggs and the fish. The most famous and expensive roe is that of the sturgeon fish which is known as CAVIARE.

ROOK HEART In mediaeval days it was a common practice to carry the heart of a rook around on the person. The story goes that during love-making, if the man has in his possession the heart of a male rook, and if the woman has in her possession the heart of a female rook, then they should always agree and live together in harmony and joy.

ROSEMARY An evergreen fragrant flowering shrub with romantic connotations causing the emotion to be overcome with a strong sensual drive. Used as a perfume and also in cookery. A great favourite of the Romans. Cleopatra is said to have bathed in asses' milk and rosemary.

RUBBER This substance is made from the sap of certain tropical trees and has a strange erotic attraction for many people who feel greatly aroused by the touch, feel and smell of rubber. Sometimes garments made of rubber are worn during love-making sessions to enhance the excitement.

RUM This is a drink associated with the Caribbean and with sailors, thus the sea-association comes into play, together with the intoxicating influences of the alcoholic content. It is distilled from sugar cane.

RUSTY NAIL This is the name given to a very potent drink consisting of a mixture of whisky and the liqueur DRAMBUIE, which gives a warm sultry feeling and an eagerness for participation in sex play.

S

SAFFLOWER A plant resembling a thistle in appearance, and once believed to be a strong sexual stimulant.

SAFFRON This is a plant of the iris family and is well known for the beautiful orange colouring agent which it contains. The colouring is used a great deal for improving many Oriental dishes and for making them look more attractive, thus the suggestion that it makes people more attractive to the opposite sex.

SAGE One of the most popular aromatic herbs used for stuffing. Need we say more.

SALMON All forms of salmon have strong aphrodisiac qualities, and in particular smoked salmon. This seems to have a marked effect on men, putting them into a mood for love.

SALT Universally accepted as a healer of mind and body, and hailed as a vigorous sex stimulant especially by the ancient Egyptians who consumed an abundance of salt meat.

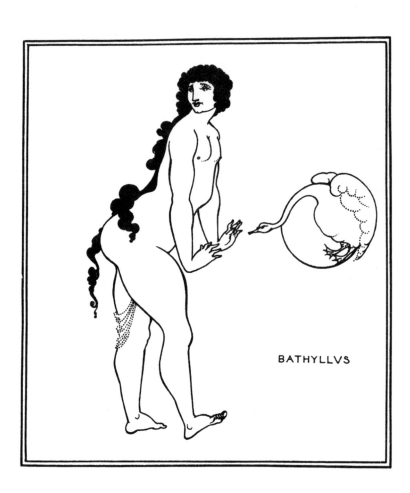

BATHYLLVS

SAMPHIRE Because this herb is found on rocks by the sea-shore, it has the mind-association with the sea. Another name for this yellow-flowered fragrant herb is 'sea-fennel'.

SANDALWOOD A yellow sweet-scented wood extensively used in the preparation of ladies' cosmetics and perfume because of its soothing effect upon the senses.

SANDIX CEROPOLIUM A plant highly regarded by the Romans as possessing the power to excite the genitals. Reported to have been used in Sweden as a sex aid.

SANGAREE Made from a mixture of spiced wine and water, this drink has the ability to heighten the sexual desires and lower the inhibitions and barriers to love-making.

SANSEVIERA A Hindu concoction made from the seeds of the plant *Sanseviera Roxburghiana* mixed with other seeds, believed to enhance sexual relationships.

SAPODILLA A large tree which is found in South America and bears a much sought-after fruit thought to enkindle the flame of passion.

SARSAPARILLA A type of climbing shrub found in the tropics. A drug is made from the root of the shrub which is taken in the form of a drink.

SASKATOON A tree found in Canada which bears small berries. These are capable of churning up a lust for sexual adventures.

SASSAFRAS An evergreen tree, the aromatic bark of which is used for medicinal purposes as well as amatory indulgences.

SATYR This creature of mythology which is half-man and half-goat and wanders the woodlands gives its name to any man known to be exceptionally lustful – thus any pictures or thoughts of the satyr leads to the mind-connection between this creature and lust.

SATYRION Much enjoyed by the Greeks and Romans, this is a plant with red leaves and a double root with an erect fleshy stem. They believed that it possessed erotic properties even when held in the hand. It was usually added to wine in order to enhance the drink. Another plant of the same family is called *Erith Raicon* which has the same provocative qualities as satyrion.

SAUSAGE Always a source of amusement, the connection between sausages and the penis was often the theme of bawdy music hall comics, and the association remains to this day due to the phallic shape.

SAVELOY This highly seasoned sausage affects the sexual awareness on two levels, firstly the mind and imagination are turned on to thoughts of the penis due to the saveloy's phallic shape, and secondly, the active ingredients have a physical effect because of the heating properties they contain.

SAVORY An aromatic herb used in cookery thought to have aphrodisiac properties by the Romans. Being hot-flavoured, it is used as a condiment. Properly known as *Satureia*.

SCALLOP Edible shellfish being rich in Vitamin E, the love vitamin, and having thought-connections with the sea-legend of Aphrodite.

SCAMMONY A gum found in the Middle East which is used for medicinal purposes. It is an especially effective aphrodisiac when mixed with honey.

SCHNAPPER A common sea fish found in Australia.

SCHNAPPS Kind of a gin drink which has devastating effect on the sexual impulses.

SEA-SLUG This creature is found in the West Indies and has a great reputation for arousing sexual interest.

SESAME Herbaceous plant popular for its seeds which give an oil thought to have wonderful and magical properties. All of a sudden the words 'open sesame' take on a new meaning.

SEX GLANDS The all-important glands that are responsible for a healthy and efficient sexual performance need first-class proteins to keep in good working order, also Vitamins A,C,E, and all the B-Vitamins, especially panthohenic acid, para-aminobenzoic acid, and folic acid. The worst troublemakers as far as the sex glands are concerned are fear and worry. Both of these depressing states could be caused by a lack of the B-Vitamins, and they could lead to greatly reduced sexual functioning, and in some extreme cases, worry could make normal functioning impossible. Tests have shown that a bad lack of the A-Vitamin, and calcium deficiency in animals can cause a marked reduction in fertility. The animals behaved in a manner which has shown that they were sexually disturbed, and in some cases there was a complete loss of LIBIDO .

SHALLOT Because of the relationship to onions, shallots are said to adopt all the aphrodisiac properties of the onion.

SHANDYGAFF Ginger and alcohol being the essence of this drink makes it a love-potion which can have profound effects. It is made by mixing ginger beer with ordinary beer.

SHERRY On a cold winter's day, nothing warms the being more than a glass of good sherry wine. It can set the soul on fire and lead to all kinds of sexual merriment.

SHIMYAAN A highly potent drink which is made in Natal and is powerful in stimulating the senses.

SHLAKSHNAPARNI A plant found in India which can be made into a sex drink guaranteed to stir up the emotions and bring on a craving for sexual gratification.

SHRIMP Shrimps are believed to have aphrodisiac qualities because of the association with the sea. However this claim does seem to be a contradiction in terms as surely the popular idea of a shrimp is something undersized, but then again it takes all kinds(!) and the shrimp does have a high Vitamin E content.

SHVADAUSTRA An Indian plant which can be pounded down to form the main ingredient in a Hindu love-potion reputed to encourage the senses towards sexual encounters.

SIREN A legendary sea nymph infamous for alluring unsuspecting sailors to their doom. There is the sea-connection here, together with the alluring element. The name of Siren is often given to a particularly alluring woman.

SKINK A small lizard found in Arab countries. Once used extensively for medicinal purposes. Hailed by the Arabs as a powerful aphrodisiac.

SKIRRET A plant with edible tubers found in Germany. A great favourite with the Romans and reputed to have been used to set a provocative scene for their many sex orgies.

SLOE GIN A liqueur which is made from sloes, the fruit of the blackthorn, rich and luxurious on the senses.

SNAIL It is believed that the snail, which is looked upon in some countries (such as France) as a delicacy, has aphrodisiac qualities.

SNAPDRAGON A colourful flower with a most unusual shaped head. Some people see it as resembling the human mouth, and others compare it with the female sex organs – it depends upon which way you look at it.

SOLE Lemon or Dover sole is a strong love food which with its sea-connection can bring waves of ecstasy and a storm of passion.

SOUTHERNWOOD A plant which the Romans regarded as a strong love token. It was believed that if the plant was placed underneath a bed, then the persons on top of the bed would find sexual fulfilment.

SOYA BEAN Becoming more and more popular as a substitute for beef because of its high protein content, the soya bean can put life and vigour into the sexual act.

SPANISH FLY 'Spanish Fly' is the popular name given to a concoction called CANTHARIDES which is made from a black beetle called *Cantharis Vesicatoria,* the beetle being dried and powdered. It was introduced to Europe from the Orient at the time of the Crusades. It can be added to drinks with devastating effects, having the power to arouse the sexual urge by acute irritation of the gastro-intestinal system and by dilation of the blood vessels, all of which stimulate the genitals. It has strong lust-inducing qualities but there is an element of danger as it can cause difficulty in urinating, blood-stained urine, and excruciating pain. It is believed that Spanish Fly is in fact a poison and it has been known that as little as 1·5 grammes can prove fatal. Tablets called 'Spanish Fly' can be bought in sex aid shops.

SPEARMINT A type of common mint with aphrodisiac properties used extensively for its flavouring powers both for medicinal and culinary purposes.

SPIKENARD An aromatic substance obtained from an Oriental plant. An ointment called FOLIATUM was prepared from this substance and was popular with the Romans as an amatory aid.

[104]

SPINACH For generations spinach has been known as the food for strength and stamina. This vegetable which can easily be grown in the garden, is surrounded by a mysterious aura of power which is believed to work wonders for the sexual appetite.

SPIRAEA A plant which is of the same family as MEADOW-SWEET, the delicately perfumed white-flowered plant believed to bring unending joy to lovers who carry the flowers while indulging in pleasures of the flesh.

SPURGE A plant which oozes a milt-like juice highly regarded for medicinal purposes. In Arab countries it is often used as an ingredient in various concoctions thought to promote sexual excitement.

STORGETHRON A plant found in Greece very similar in appearance to the leek. By Greek tradition, if this plant is served either in solid or liquid form, it promotes love-play.

STRAMONIUM A herb properly known as *Datura Stramonium* and sometimes nicknamed THORN APPLE. Widely used in the Orient as an aphrodisiac. A drug is extracted from the plant which can cause sexually-tinted hallucinations. Can be dangerous if taken in large quantities.

STRAWBERRY The small red juicy fruit has associations in the mind with the female sex organs. As well as this claim to fame, it is rich in Vitamin B2.

STURGEON The fish from which CAVIARE is obtained. Very highly regarded as a sexual stimulant, especially around the Mediterranean countries where sturgeon soup is a speciality.

SUGAR Accepted as a sweetening agent the world over, it is a vegetable substance which can be obtained from various plants such as sugar-beet or sugar-cane. The name given to an elderly man who showers presents upon a young woman of the gold-digging variety, is a 'sugardaddy'.

SUNFLOWER SEED The large golden sunflower drinks in goodness from the sunshine and the seeds have great health-giving properties and bring a sunny disposition to lovers, making them happy and contented.

SURAG A root plant which has a reputation for being capable of arousing lust.

SWEETFLAG The popular name given to *Calamus Aromaticus* which was a popular mediaeval exciter of the flesh, widely used in love philtres and amorous concoctions.

SWEET POTATO The common name for YAM, a large edible tuber which is reputed to provoke lustful tendencies.

SYLLABUB When served after a hearty fortifying meal, this dish which consists of sugar, cream and wine will whip up desire and set the mood for love.

T

TALLOW The melted fat of an animal which is believed to bring staggering results when applied to the sexual parts of both partners before love-play.

TARO A plant found in the romantic South Sea Islands. The roots can be eaten or pulped into a drink believed to bring charm and enticement to all in love.

TARPON A large fish found around the Florida coast of America which is believed to be aphrodisiac by its sea-association.

TARRAGON Another aromatic herb used for culinary purposes which can boost a man's appetite for food and love. Tarragon is said to have powers to arouse sexual desire. A special drink can be made from this herb called 'Tarragona' — two glasses of this and anyone's a gonner.

THORN APPLE The common name given to STRAMONIUM, a drug which is popular in the Orient and can cause erotic dreams and hallucinations. Dangerous if taken in excess.

THYME An aromatic herb with sensual overtones used to add flavour and lift to many dishes as it is particularly conducive to the health of a man's body.

THYROID This is the lump located at the front of the throat, which is responsible for an active successful sex life. Popularly known as the 'Adam's apple', this story goes back to the Garden of Eden when Eve tempted Adam with an apple. When he succumbed to her seductions the apple was supposed to have stuck in his throat, and from that day to this, all men have a lump in the front of their throats. The function of the thyroid is to secrete a hormone called 'thyroxine' into the bloodstream which stimulates the sex glands. If the thyroid is underactive, weak or lazy the condition is called 'hypothyroidism' and results in a weak sex drive and can cause obesity due to the vast amount of water which is sometimes retained in the body. On the other hand, if the thyroid is overactive, the tendency is to become oversexed. It is reported that Mae West had an overactive or 'double' thyroid and that accounted for her reputation. However there are certain side-effects which come from an overactive thyroid which include an interruption of the menstrual cycle, and a tendency to suffer from nervous fatigue.

The thyroid also controls the metabolism and a deficiency of the hormone thyroxine reduces the need for calories, and causes mental sluggishness, difficulty in remembering, and a constant desire to sleep. If the thyroid becomes enlarged due to a lack of iodine in the diet, it produces a condition called 'goitre' which is a swelling in the neck. Although goitre is not in itself dangerous, it is the body's way of showing that there is real trouble ahead. At the first sign of any swelling in the front of the neck, a doctor should be called without delay. The symptoms of

[108]

goitre can be relieved with a strong Vitamin B diet found in brewer's yeast and liver. The thyroid can become weakened due to a lack of iodine causing the toxic goitre condition, and in this case, large doses of iodine are necessary, as are other nutrients such as copper, calcium, and magnesium. A healthy thyroid is of the utmost importance for sex as it is the beautifier of the body, giving healthy hair, strong nails, and a good complexion. It keeps us slim, trim and alert, sexually aware and active, leading to a fuller happier life. An unhealthy thyroid leads to depression, fear, worry, a weakened sex drive, and can result in an appearance of old age before the time. The best foods for a healthy thyroid are:

Protein – found in meat, eggs, cheese and fortified milk.
B-vitamin – found in brewer's yeast, yogurt, wheatgerm, liver, dark molasses.
Iodine – iodized salt, preferably iodized vegetable salt.

TIA MARIA The rum-based liqueur which heats the blood and encourages bouts of sensual indulgence.

TOKAY A type of wine from a place in Hungary of the same name which is believed to send the sex organs into quivering ecstasy.

TOMATO As far back as the sixteenth century, Mexicans held the tomato in great esteem because of the erotic powers it was believed to possess. This could have been attributed to the fact that the round plump appearance could be linked in the mind to the male organs. It was sometimes known as a 'love-apple'.

TONKA A drug which is extracted from tonquin beans, the seeds of a plant called *Coumarouna Odorata*. The beans are bitter-tasting but because of their delicate perfume they are widely used as a flavouring agent in cookery. The drug is believed to possess aphrodisiac properties.

TRAPA BISPINOSA A plant, the roots of which are used in a strong Hindu love-potion. The plant is somewhat similar to the water chestnut.

TRIPE The stomach of an animal which is widely believed to be highly nutritious, and to possess aphrodisiac properties.

TRUFFLE This food is an edible fungus which grows underground and is one of the best known aphrodisiacs. Very popular in France especially around the Strasbourg area where they have a special market exclusively for the sale of truffles. This food has a great reputation for arousing passion and was said to have been eaten by Casanova to sustain him through his lustful escapades.

TURMERIC An Indian plant the root of which is powdered down and used as a medicine and condiment. It can also be used as a dye.

TURNIP The widely-used root vegetable hailed as an aphrodisiac in France when served in a concoction of beef and parsley. Also, it is the accepted accompanying dish for HAGGIS which in itself is believed to be an aphrodisiac.

UV

UCHCHATA A plant found in India, the root of which is highly prized as an ingredient for a Hindu love-potion.

UDDERS In mediaeval days it was customary for butchers to sell the udders of the sow. It was believed that if they were hung up in the bedroom or any place where the sex act was to be performed, then it would bring on a tumult of lust to the proceedings.

UNICORN Mysterious creature of mythology. A horse with a single twisted horn growing out of the top of its head. Looked upon as having magical and incredible powers and because of the phallic horn shape, believed to have aphrodisiac qualities.

URID The seeds of an Indian plant which are soaked in milk and sugar. These are made into cakes and eaten each morning to promote vigorous sexual activity.

VALERIAN A flowering herb which is believed to have aphrodisiac properties, and is widely used for medicinal purposes.

BATHYLLVS

VANILLA The plant of this name is a member of the ORCHID family, the flower of love. The essence from the vanilla is widely used for flavouring purposes. It is included in the list of aphrodisiacs because of its smell which somewhat resembles the aroma of the female sex secretions. Also the ancient Romans looked upon the vanilla root as being similar in appearance to the vaginal canal. It is reported that the name 'vanilla' was sometimes mistaken in the olden days for the word 'vagina', and thereby hangs a tale.

VATODBHRANTA A plant, the leaves of which can be powdered down and used as an aphrodisiac cream.

VEAL A very substantial food having many health-giving properties, not the least of which is that it keeps the sex organs maintained and in full working order. If eaten with wine and cream, both aphrodisiacs in their own right, the consequences could be enchanting.

VENISON The flesh of the deer which is believed to have aphrodisiac properties. It is said to have been eaten by Robin Hood and his Merry Men in Sherwood Forest, and by all accounts, Maid Marian was happy enough with her love life.

VERMICELLI This is a type of macaroni from romantic Italy which when eaten is said to bring on a feeling for love which teases the imagination.

VERMOUTH The extremely popular aperitif which is flavoured from the WORMWOOD herb and is famous for coaxing the senses into a romantic mood and ready for love.

VIBRATOR A long thin instrument which is battery-operated and vibrates in a way designed to give the user pleasure. It can be used by both sexes, but is mostly used by the female, although one of the most popular vibrators on the market has four interchangeable heads to stimulate both the female and male partners in versatile ways which truly amaze. Various types of this gadget can be got in sex supermarkets. They come in all colours, shapes and sizes and they are designed to tickle the imagination, to say the least. And are addictive.

VINEGAR Being the acid residue from wine and other alcoholic liqueurs, vinegar possesses a certain amount of aphrodisiac properties. A kind of hangover from the wine. The Arabs make a special pastry from honey, vinegar and various herbs and spices which is believed to strengthen the sexual awareness.

VIRILITY PILL As described earlier, this comes in the form of the KEITAFO BANLON tablet, from China.

VITAMINS Necessary for good health and therefore happy love-making. Vitamin C prevents colds and is plentiful in all fresh fruit and vegetables. Vitamin E is known as the love and youth vitamin and promotes vitality and the efficient function-ing of nerves and muscles, it is found in wheatgerm and milk. Vitamin B2, gives a feeling of general well-being, healthy hair and clear bright eyes. Vitamin B12, is essential for stamina and is found in yeast, liver, spinach, eggs, lettuce and meat. Multivitamin tablets can be got at all chemists and they are a sure way of making certain of a well-balanced vitamin intake.

VODKA From Russia with love, providing it is not served with lime, comes this very popular drink which is distilled from rye or potatoes. Some of its popularity might rest in the fact that this spirit can be taken without leaving any trace of a smell on the breath, therefore would-be infidels and debauchees could go about their business without fear of blowing their cover, as it were.

MESSALINA.

W

WATAMA Japanese women indulge in *Watama* which means that they insert two metal balls into the vagina. One ball is light and one heavy, and the lightest of the two is inserted first. They are both filled with QUICKSILVER, and at every moment when the two balls meet, they send out vibrating quivers which produce sensations of ecstasy.

WEESIL The ashes of the weesil were in great demand in Elizabethan times. Apparently if weesil ash was annointed on the big toe of the right foot, mixed with honey, it would effect a cure for impotency.

WHEATGERM Germ of the wheat cereal plant, chiefly used in bread-making. Very rich in Vitamin E, the love vitamin, and always recommended for an active sex-life.

WHITING A popular edible sea fish which has the mind-association with the sea and the goddess Aphrodite.

WILD POPPY Believed to be an aphrodisiac, possibly due to the connection with opium, the dangerous drug which can set the mind reeling and which is known to cause erotic dreams.

WILD RUE A plant that is found in Australia from the seeds of which HARMINE is extracted. This is a highly dangerous drug which can produce hallucinations of an erotic nature.

WINE Good wine has always been regarded as a drink to mellow the senses and prepare the body and mind for love.

WINKLE This shellfish has a double claim to being an aphrodisiac firstly because of the sea-connection, and secondly because of the name 'winkle' which is a nickname for the penis. It was believed that by eating the small winkle it would add measure to its namesake and help it to become upstanding.

WITCH-HAZEL A versatile shrub with yellow flowers. The seeds can be eaten alone, or powdered down and mixed with honey and milk and served as a love philtre. The leaves and bark are dried and used extensively in cosmetic preparations. The shrub has a double aphrodisiac attraction, being used both internally and externally.

WOODCOCK A bird resembling a snipe which is a great culinary speciality and is believed to hold strong aphrodisiac powers.

WOODRUFF A plant found in woodland areas with small white fragrant flowers, believed to hold powers as a love token.

WORMWOOD A herb used extensively in the preparation of alcoholic drinks due to its bitter flavour. Believed to be a strong aphrodisiac especially when mixed with alcohol.

XYZ

X-FILMS Pornographic films which arouse the sexual desire. They cater for all tastes and the subjects dealt with include heterosexuality, homosexuality, lesbianism, troilism, etc.

YAM The name given to the sweet potato and believed to possess aphrodisiac powers.

YARROW A herb with a strong perfume and astringent properties. In mediaeval times it was a tradition for honeymooners to wear a yarrow spray to ensure a long and healthy love life.

YEAST The substance used as a fermenting agent, brewer's yeast, is recommended as a sex stimulant and is fairly inexpensive. Its main characteristic is its amazing rising powers and this has the mind-association with the rising of the penis into an erection, ready for sex.

YELLOW SANDERS A substance which was used in mediaeval times as an aphrodisiac ingredient in various love potions. See RED SANDERS.

YELLOW-WOOD A tree found in South Africa and believed to cast an aphrodisiac lure over the natives.

YEW An evergreen tree, the dark leaves of which are believed to enliven the amatory urge.

YOGA SLANT BOARD For a complete body overhaul and increased sexual prowess, lying upside down on a yoga slant board is highly recommended. It is easy to build a slant board, which is simply a strong board made from either solid wood or strong plastic. It can be lined with foam for extra comfort. The board should be eighteen inches across by about six feet long (longer if required), and should be raised at the feet end by twelve or fifteen inches. This can be done by making small legs, and attaching them to the board, or by simply placing the feet end on top of a small chair or stool. It is important to note that this end should under no circumstances be raised any higher than fifteen inches, otherwise it could become dangerous. The aim is to lie on the board for one minute a day, increasing to a total of fifteen minutes a day by gradually adding a minute a day. In this way it is possible to get all the benefits of head-standing without any of the dangers associated with this activity, i.e. broken collar bones etc. By using the natural pull of gravity, the yoga board helps to correct faulty posture, double chins, and spare tyres. A dragging face will receive a free face-lift quicker and more naturally than by any other method. It adjusts the spine and inner organs to the correct line by way of the bloodstream. It relaxes all muscles and supplies blood to the vital centres of the body. It reduces the waistline, and abdominal muscles because of the reversed pull of gravity. It reduces swollen limbs by taking the weight completely off the legs and feet. The benefits of using a yoga slant board are enormous. It improves the circulation and gives a clear fresh complexion, shining hair and an all-over attractiveness. It reduces face tension and wrinkles. It is reported that the brain functions at the rate of 14% better when the head is lower than the feet. This practice is most effective if performed for fifteen minutes a day, twice a day, and can be carried out at any time, but it is recommended that the best time is on coming home from work in the evening in a tired and weary state. When lying on the board, a good exercise is to draw in the stomach muscles and count to ten. This is especially good for the waistline. For busy people, a quick way of dealing with exercises is to practise one very strong maximum contraction twice a day.

YOGURT A most popular and nourishing preparation of separated milk which has excellent health values. It can be enhanced by the addition of various types of fresh fruit, and adds a zest to the sex side of life.

YOHIMBINE Before modern drug and hormone treatment became available, yohimbine was the most widely-used stimulant for increasing the sexual drive. This was a crystalline alkaloid substance derived from the bark of the yohimbe tree, found in Africa and has long been a favourite with the natives. It creates its effect by stimulating the nerves of the spinal column, which in turn, stimulates the genitals. It is used in veterinary medicine to excite bulls and stallions. The technical name for this sex potion is *Corynantle Yohimbe*.

ZULU A member of the African tribe of the Bantu stock who are believed to have fed on YOHIMBINE which is a strong sex food. The Zulu is reputed to be endowed with extra large sexual organs and a super-powered sex drive.